To Rupert

Lots of ?

From Great Auntie
Hazel

x x x

This book has been based on the true happenings at 'Bide a Wee' my home for over twenty years. It had a beautiful garden which brought me a lot of happiness plus a lot of hard work! The wild life etc became the characters for my book, it's been a joy getting it all together!

I thank those who supported and inspired me to write the rhyming stories.

Author
Hazel M Foster

Animal and Garden

Adventures

Hunsy, Thumps and Friends!

Volume 2

Author

Hazel M Foster

Illustrator

Dawn S Taylor

ISBN 978-0-9957755-1-0

Thumps

'Bide a Wee'

Hunsy and Thumps say "Hello"
There are still lots of jobs to do!
Others friends have joined them
Who would like to meet you too

Lady

Hunsy

Contents

Jack Frost

The flowers. shivered in their pots whispering to each other
"It's really cold and damp out here we should be undercover"
Jack was up bright and early, spreading his blanket around!
It glistened in the sunlight, he'd covered most of the ground.

Hunsy rescued the flower pots, covering them with fleece
She lined them up against the hedge, to winter there in peace
When Jack feels cold and frosty, he settles on everything!
He stays around, all winter long, right up to early spring.

Leaves had fallen from the trees, they were piled high!
Hunsy raked up all she could, beneath the cloudy grey sky
With winter time approaching, the nights were drawing in
Pip the squirrel buried his nuts, birds were on the wing.

Hunsy stays warm and cozy in her home at 'Bide a Wee'
Her friends are always there for her, they keep her company
When the sun shines down on Jack, he slowly melts away!
If it's freezing he comes back - to reign another day.

Beaky the Pigeon moans!

Beaky shivered in the cold "This is crazy weather" he said
"Its springtime now and we have snow, the wintertime I dread
All us birds, we would starve to death, if Hunsy wasn't there!
She makes sure we're all well fed, with lots of food to share".

Hunsy was putting the rubbish out, "Hello Beaky" she said
"It's freezing out, it's bitterly cold, I'll toss you out some bread"
She tore a slice into pieces, then she tossed it from her window
Beaky made his way across, leaving claw marks in the snow.

He gulped the bread down hastily, Patsy his mate wanted some
Beaky turned round and chased her away, he had her on the run
Hunsy saw what was happening, "Don't be so greedy" she said
"You must learn to share your food, I've got plenty of bread".

Beaky flew away and sulked, he hated England's cold weather!
"Thumps is flying to Florida, maybe we could fly there together"
"Stop acting so silly" said Hunsy, "You could never fly that fast!
The sun will warm your feathers - this snow's not going to last".

Suzie the Sun

Hunsy's waiting for Suzie, "We need the sun" she said
"When it's cold and cloudy, I don't want to get out of bed
The winter time seems long and cold, when Frosty is about
I always look forward to summertime, as I prefer to be out".

The flower pots were sleeping all covered up with fleece
Leaves had fallen from the trees, growth it seems to cease!
Hunsy always feeds the birds, Beaky the pigeon's well fed
He likes sitting on the fence, waiting patiently for his bread.

Donnie the fish he doesn't eat, throughout the winter time
Hunsy keeps him undercover, until the weather turns fine
The other fish stay close to him, as he's head of the family
Hector the heron's no longer a threat, he fishes out at sea.

When Suzie the sun arrives, the ground it starts to warm
The other plants begin to grow, when the daffodils perform!
A blaze of yellow everywhere, in fields and gardens green
Suzie shines down brightly - enhancing a beautiful scene.

Wally the Wheelbarrow

Wally was leaning against the shed, he felt rather cold
"These frosty nights are getting to me, making me feel old
I've never felt like this before, I need a cozy warm bed!
Is there any room for me, to sleep in Hunsy's shed?"

Wally always works so hard, he helps with many jobs
He's very strong and made of steel, he carries heavy logs
His tyre is made of rubber, it helps him to bounce along
The day that it deflated, he wondered what was wrong.

"I've got a problem" said Wally, "I can't work today
My tyre is flat and crumpled it makes me want to sway!"
"I'll have a look" said Hunsy, "You really must get going
I need to cut the hedges today, they're forever growing".

Thumps came to the rescue, he patched him up that day
Wally was able to work again, all his fears had gone away
When winter time approaches, leaves fall from the trees
Wally slept in Hunsy's shed - he didn't want to freeze.

Toby the Toad

Hunsy was clearing the garden, she had lots of work to do!
Where do I start? she said to herself, some work was overdue
She started by cutting some shrubs back, it was early spring
"Everything's a mess" she said, "Look the trees are budding".

Jimmy the jet wash said, "I'm going to wash this dirt away
The patio looks really filthy, it will need a very strong spray"
He jet washed everything in sight, Hunsy was very impressed
She knew she could rely on him, as he always did his best.

"I've painted the hog house green" Hunsy proudly said!
She knocked on Henry's little door, "He must be still in bed"
When she looked inside his house, she got a great big shock
Toby sat there grinning, "I'm the new kid on the block".

"This is Henry's house" said Hunsy, "You are trespassing"
"I've got squatters rights" he said, "And you can't do a thing"
"Oh yes I can" said Hunsy, "It's full up with rubbish inside!
Jimmy said he'll hose it down" - "I'm leaving!" Toby cried.

The Garden Gnomes

Hunsy has so many friends, she loves the garden gnomes
They all live here at 'Bide a Wee' each has their own homes
They stay in smart log cabins, their lights are on all night
Others know that they are there, it's such a pretty sight.

They work hard every day, it lasts the whole year through
Digging the garden, felling the trees, gathering leaves up too
Logs are used to build their homes, they stay cozy and warm
They must prepare for winter time, in case there is a storm.

Brendan is their governor, you never hear him moaning!
He strums all day on his guitar, Hunsy loves to hear him sing
He makes sure the gnomes are happy, when they go to work
With plenty of things for them to do, it doesn't pay to shirk.

Little Joe he never stops, he works the whole day long
He built the roof, over the pond, he made it nice and strong
When evening time comes around, all the gnomes relax!
Lady loves to visit them - they don't mind pussycats.

Charlie the Chain Saw

"Charlie's coming round today," Stan the strimmer said
"Thumps needs him to cut the trees, a few of them are dead
They'll have to climb up a ladder, the trees are quite a height
If I climbed up, I'd fall down, they'll need to hold on tight".

Thumps put Charlie in his van, "We're off to 'Bide a Wee'
Hunsy needs our help today, she makes us a good of cup tea"
Charlie was very excited, "I'll be meeting my friends again
I can't wait to cut those trees, we're hoping it doesn't rain".

Hunsy was pleased to see them, "I really hate those trees!
I can't climb up a ladder now, heights they make me freeze"
Thumps put Charlie in the shed, his pals were having a rest
Harvey the Hover he couldn't work, his face was in a mess.

He has had a nasty accident, and fallen down on his nose
The front of his face had broken up, "I've had it I suppose"
Charlie tried to cheer him up, "You must look after yourself
There's always plastic surgery - on the National Health".

Whirly the Wind

The wind kept howling all around, up and down the street
Whirly was really enjoying himself, "I'm having such a treat"
He whistled around the houses, lifting tiles from the roof tops
"I'm really having fun" he said, "I'm hoping this never stops".

Hunsy looked out from her window, trees swayed to and fro!
Whirly had blown the branches down, some were hanging low
She ran down the garden, Fred the shed was shaking with fear
Whirly had ripped his door off, the weather was very severe.

He chased her around the garden, "I'll make you lose your hat"
She clung on to it desperately but he blew and that was that!
He blew it down the garden, and left it hanging there on a tree
Hunsy was getting very upset, "That hat was a present for me".

Whirly kept on blowing for hours, he tried to wreck everything!
The garden now looked an awful mess, Whirly enjoyed his fling
Thumps called in to see her, "Don't worry I'll help you manage
Whirly had no right to do this - it's a case of criminal damage".

Binny the Dustbin

Binny was feeling despondent, "I'm almost redundant" he said
"I'm full up with dead leaves and rubbish, the future I really dread
I'm fed up with all this recycling, colored boxes for this and for that!
They argue about their collection days, all I hear is their yackety yak".

"Whirly the wind has a lot of fun, he blows them down the street
He rips off their lids, tin cans bounce around, playing hide and seek
The boxes end up with somebody else, with lids that don't even fit!
It's a waste of money" said Binny, "I did the job twice as quick".

"Hunsy puts a black sack in me, then all the old rubbish goes in
The men collect the sacks every week, she doesn't need a dustbin!
I never go out the front now, I used to enjoy being carried around
I'm left with no one to talk to, I'm stuck here on the ground".

"My Granddad's made of metal, he's always been very strong
He got filled up with everything, there were no rights or wrong!
Things aint like they used to be - my Granddad he loves to say
I'll need to work for as long as I can, as I'll be retired one day".

Molly the Moth

Hunsy was feeling rather cold, "It's very chilly" she said
"I'm going to put a jumper on, and my favorite colour is red"
She opened up the cupboard door, Molly was sitting inside
"What are you doing" cried Hunsy, "Are you trying to hide?"

"Your light attracted me", said Molly "I kept flying around
Then I noticed your cupboard, I slept there without a sound
My larva they were hungry, they needed something to chew!
They found your red jumper tasty, I saw that it looked new".

Hunsy put her red jumper on, she found it was full of holes
"I can't wear this, Molly's ruined it, it's like it's got peepholes?"
Molly looked really guilty, "It's the fashion they wear today!
The jeans have holes in the knees, I've seen them on display".

"I'm not a model" said Hunsy, "I just need something warm
You must leave here right away" Molly then started to yawn!
"I'm feeling rather tired just now, I could leave here tomorrow?
Charity shops have jumpers, I'm sure they'd let you borrow".

Hunsy Paints 'Bide a Wee'

Hunsy was ready for painting, "The walls look so dirty" she said
"I'll be using some snowy white paint, as the tiles on the roof are red
I can paint the lower half, and then Thumps he could paint up the top!
He'll need to use Lofty the ladders, if you fall it's a very long drop".

When Thumps called in to see her, she told him about her plans!
He then agreed to help her but said "There are some very wide spans
I'll need to use Ronnie the roller, I could buy him a thick fluffy coat!
He loves painting rough stone walls, he's a very hard working bloke".

Hunsy was feeling really pleased, she couldn't wait to start the job
She'd bought a load of white paint, it's expensive so costs a few bob!
She started painting the very next day, the walls looked snowy white
Then it suddenly poured with rain, it went on throughout the night.

A lot of the paint got washed off the walls, Hunsy was most upset
Thumps called round, he'd broken his wrist, the job now under threat!
But he didn't give up that easily, he tied Ronnie, to an extension pole
He managed to reach right to the top - this got them out of trouble.

Lofty the Ladders

Hunsy started her painting again, "I can't reach" she said
She stood there on a ladder, with her arms above her head!
"This wall it does need painting, I need someone who's tall
If I should loose my balance, I could be heading for a fall".

Thumps called round to see her, "Hello Hunsy" he said
"I thought you were feeling poorly, and resting in your bed
Your arm it won't get better, you'll give yourself more pain"
He knew she never listened, his advice was always in vain.

"I need your help" said Hunsy, "I'm safer on the ground!
You could paint where I can't reach, we need Lofty round"
Thumps called back with Lofty, tied to the top of his van
He was happy to help out, things went according to plan.

Lofty is slim and very tall, he extends to twice his height!
He's made of aluminium, it's a metal that's strong and light
When he leans against the wall, Thumps climbs to the top
But if you have a fear of heights - it's really quite a drop!

Annie the Ant

Annie was very busy, there were ant hills everywhere
"They'll ruin my grass" said Hunsy, she began to despair!
She scraped the top of an ant hill, Annie looked up and said
"Be careful or you'll damage our nest, this is a baby egg".

"You can't stay here" said Hunsy, "You will have to move
Thumps is coming here later on, and I know he'll disapprove
I feel like I'm being invaded, I've seen many more like you!
I know you all work very hard, you must have lots to do".

"We have to work hard" said Annie, "I belong to an army
We help the Queen's prepare for flight, everyone goes barmy
The ants with wings fly off together, they mate on the wing!
The eggs are kept safe underground, laid there in early spring".

"I'm sad for you" said Hunsy "But its better that you leave
Thumps has got some Ant Stop, there won't be any reprieve!
If I were you, I'd leave right now, I'm giving you a chance"
"Not to worry" said Annie, "We're marching on to France".

Relining the Pond

Hunsy depends a lot on Thumps, he always helps her out
She consults him with everything, whenever she's in doubt
One day she was despairing, as the pond had sprung a leak
Donnie the fish was worried, as things looked very bleak.

Hunsy put tap water in the pond but sadly two fish died!
"What can I do" she said to Thumps, then he quickly replied
"Don't worry Hunsy, I'll fix it, this pond it must be relined
I'm going to remove all the fish, none of them will mind".

Everything went smoothly, Thumps had a paddling pool
He placed the fish in gently, they all thought it really cool!
"It's great to be here on holiday", said Donnie with a smile
The sun was shining brightly, things were done in style.

Thumps relined the pond, then he filled it with water again
They netted the fish, one by one, none of them suffered pain
They all swam around contented, the pond looked beautiful
Lady the cat she sat by and watched - a perfect day for all.

Screwy the Screwdriver

Screwy was really worried, "I can't work" he said
"Every time I start to screw, I feel so dizzy in my head"
Hunsy tried to comfort him, "There's work for you to do
I want a cabinet on my wall, it won't stay up with glue".

Thumps came with his toolbox, "I need Screwy" he said
"I cannot find him anywhere, surly he's not still in bed?"
Screwy lay there shivering, he wanted to get up and work
Most of the jobs rely on him, he would never try to shirk.

Hunsy opened up the drawer, "You must try to screw!
Don't give up too easily, as there's so much work to do"
Thumps said, "Not to worry, I'm going to examine him
He shouldn't be feeling so dizzy, his head all in a spin".

Thumps soon saw the problem, he removed his head
"He needs a Philips screw, for different work" he said
Screwy no longer felt dizzy, he screwed away all day
All the work got finished - his fears had gone away.

Panic in the Pond

Donnie the fish was worried, "Where is Hunsy" he said
"The pond pumps they have failed, soon we'll all be dead!
We need oxygen to stay alive", his mates swam close behind
"This must be sorted" said Donnie, "I'll see what I can find".

When he looked, he could see the water had stopped flowing
"We need help before it's too late, I'll try to get things going"
Hunsy was feeling uneasy, "I need to check the pond outside"
She wandered down the garden, "Help us!" poor Donnie cried.

Hunsy tried to fix things but she could not start the pumps!
She felt so helpless on her own, "It's another job for Thumps"
She ran a long lead from the house, this got them out of trouble
Donnie breathed a sigh of relief, as he heard the water bubble.

Thumps came round to help her, "The pond it needs rewiring!
Don't worry Hunsy, I can fix it, we can't risk more fish dying"
Thumps returned with his toolbox, he soon got things put right
All the fish were safe again - they'd suffered an awful fright.

Up for Sale!

"'Bide a Wee' is up for sale", shouted Hector the heron!
He'd seen the sale notice board, around about half past seven
"Good morning everyone" he said, "I've got a big surprise!
You lot will be homeless soon", he grinned with beady eyes.

"You're joking!" said Pip the squirrel, "Hunsy wouldn't sell"
"Oh yes she would" Hector jeered, "Be careful you almost fell
I'm off to inform all the others" Pip he looked really worried!
He gathered up some tasty nuts, back to his home he scurried.

The news spread very quickly, it made everyone feel sad
Donnie the fish said to his mates "Things must be really bad!
Does Hunsy know what she's doing, she said she'd never sell?
She must have a very good reason but has chosen not to tell".

Lady the cat was anxious, she could see that Hunsy despaired
She cuddled up close to comfort her, as everything they shared
"Things will work out" said Lady, "We can't stay here forever
You will never be lonely - we'll always stay close together".

'Bide a Wee' Plans!

Hunsy was in for an awful shock, no way did she foresee
There were plans to build on land, surrounding 'Bide a Wee'
Everyone they shook with fear, what did this really mean?
How could anyone, ever accept, such an outrageous scene?

She consulted Thumps at once, he gave her sound advice
"Wait and see what happens" he said, sounding very precise
An access road was planned, to replace the home next door!
More traffic noise and fumes, who knows what's in store?

Hunsy thought of all her friends, "We want peace and quiet
I'm going to tell Kevin the cockerel, to cause a great big riot
There must be a way to get it stopped, we must all complain"
Ollie the owl very wisely said, "The plans were quite insane".

They all stood up, in the court, to give their points of view
Pip the squirrel argued, "They will chop our tree down too"
The meeting it soon ended, the plans had all been refused!
Ollie stood up and hooted - the judge was not amused.

Bobby the Blackbird

Bobby was flying too and fro, "I love cherries" he said
"They're very ripe and juicy, now they have turned red"
Hunsy was planning a big party, "I'll make a cherry pie
All my friends are welcome, even Bluey the blowfly".

She tidied around her garden, saying to Donnie the fish
"We're going to have a party, I'll be making a tasty dish
Will you do your dolphin act, and put on a special show
Entertainment is top of the list, as it makes a party flow".

Hunsy was very excited, the time was running out fast!
'Bide a Wee' looked beautiful, Suzie the sun was forecast
The fruit trees bore some apples, the plum tree was the best
Winnie the wasp ate all she could, she used them as a nest.

Thumps paid Hunsy a visit, "Have you made those pies?"
She went into the garden but she couldn't believe her eyes
All the cherries had disappeared, "What am I going to do"
Bobby had one in his beak, "I've saved this one for you".

Celebration Party!

Hunsy was feeling overjoyed, Ollie the owl won his case
Everyone, felt so relieved, knowing their homes were safe!
"I'm not selling" said Hunsy, "You are all welcome to stay
'Bide a Wee' it is our home", all her fears had gone away.

"Let's have a garden party" said Hunsy, "We will celebrate
I won't invite Hector the heron, he's caused a lot of heartache"
Everyone they clapped and laughed, "He has himself to blame
Ollie was right, when he said, the plans were quite insane".

"Hector was hoping to rule the roost, he tried to drive us away
He wanted to move his family in, as the fish would be easy prey
We've got lots of work to do, Ted the tractor will cut the grass
Thumps will be pleased to hear the news, peace again at last".

They all enjoyed the party, Bluey the blowfly, he popped in!
He landed on Hunsy's sandwich "I love eating tasty chicken"
"I forgot to invite you" said Hunsy, "You've still got dirty feet"
"Spit and polish will do" said Bluey, "This is a special treat".

Mozzy the Mosquito

Mozzy flew around boasting, "I've bitten Hunsy" he said
"She didn't know that it was me, she was resting on her bed"
Hunsy started to really itch, she was bitten from head to toe!
"Did anyone see the culprit, someone should surely know?".

Mozzy went away and hid, then met up with all his mates
"Have you heard the news" he said, "About the garden fetes?
They go on till midnight, there'll be plenty of people around
We'll bite as many as we can, we'll hover near the ground."

Hunsy was busy feeding the fish, Mozzy hovered close by
"You'll get bitten" said Donnie the fish, "I could be your spy"
"It's okay for you" said Hunsy, "Mosquito's can't really swim
You're safe there in the water, they always bite people's skin".

Mozzy flew over to say Hello, "Good evening Hunsy" he said
"It's very late for you to be out, you'd be better off in your bed"
"I'm covered in spots" said Hunsy, "The itching drives me mad"
"Whoever bit you is nasty" he said, "They must be very bad".

Renee the Rain

Hunsy was watering her garden, she used Hoppy the hose
"I've been waiting for Renee" she said, "Heaven only knows
Everything needs watering, now the grass is drying up too!
We've had sunshine every day, the skies are always blue".

"My water butts are empty, I've cleaned out all the muck
If only it would pour with rain, maybe the jet streams stuck!
Renee's really enjoying herself, she's pouring down in Wales
Whirly the wind is helping her, he's causing awful gales".

Hunsy tried digging the garden but the fork it wouldn't go in
The ground was so hard she gave up, the plants needed watering
Willy the worm said, "Don't worry, we all need Renee the Rain
I think she's away on holiday, I've heard she's in sunny Spain".

Ted the tractor was feeling fed up, it was very hot in the shed!
He really wanted to cut the grass, "Why isn't it growing?" he said
Hunsy tried to explain to him, "We're waiting for Renee the Rain
When she returns and soaks everything, the grass will grow again".

Hoppy the Hose

Hoppy is very important, he gets used for everything!
Hunsy always relies on him, especially in early spring
There are so many jobs for him, he's always on the go
When Hunsy turns the tap on, his water starts to flow.

"I'm all ready" said Hoppy, "I will water the flowers
Hunsy likes to prop me up, I end up working for hours"
Willy the worm said, "It's raining I'll put my raincoat on
Susie the sun is shining, where's this rain coming from?"

"It's only me" said Hoppy, "The ground seems very dry
I've got to do the watering, we don't want the plants to die
Reenie the rain was forecast but she's away on a holiday!
The water butts are empty, the skies they're turning grey".

"Hopefully she will turn up, I could really do with a rest!
A hose-pipes job is never done, I always try to do my best
When I wash the patios, Jimmy the jet wash, he helps me
We work wonders together but his motor is rather noisy".

The Bird Bath

"Beaky's squatting in the bath", Tiny the blue tit said
"He makes the water dirty, and he's eaten all our bread"
"No I haven't" said Beaky, "Why should I take the blame
I'm going to see Ollie the owl, he will clear my name".

Beaky didn't want to move, "I think you're being mean
The bird baths here for all of us, the water's always clean!
Hunsy fills it every day, with fresh rainwater from the sky
We need to keep our feathers clean, so that we can fly".

Tiny wasn't satisfied, "I'm going to arrange a meeting
Everyone's invited, we'll make sure there's no cheating!
All us birds we need to bathe, Beaky must learn to share
I really don't like arguments, it always brings despair".

Ollie the owl he hooted, "I'll hear your points of view
You must answer honestly, don't let me hear you argue"
One by one, they all spoke out, it didn't take them long!
All agreed to share the bath - with no one in the wrong.

Dickey and Dottie the Ducks

Hunsy was feeling poorly, she was in for a big surprise
She opened her front door, she couldn't believe her eyes!
Dickey and Dottie were there, "Are you better?" they said
"We wanted to pay you a visit but you were still in bed".

"I know" said Hunsy, "I felt poorly but I have work to do
I have got some tasty bread, would you like to step through?"
They were friendly and hungry, they gobbled up the bread
Beaky the pigeon joined them, "It's a lovely day" he said.

They sat on the grass and sunbathed, it was a perfect day
Hunsy didn't want them to go, she said that they could stay
But they were living somewhere else, a farm across the way
George the gardener cut the grass, they had to waddle away.

They will always be welcome, if they come to her front door
Hunsy hopes they'll visit again, she hadn't seen them before!
Friends are most important, it's nice to have them call round
You can find them anywhere - above or beneath the ground.

Hunsy's Runner Beans

Hunsy felt disappointed, "My beans won't grow" she said
"I've got loads of orange flowers, I keep them all well fed"
"Don't you worry" said Thumps, "You need Bertie the bee!
He'll pollinate the flowers for you, he does it all for free".

Bertie called round that evening, "Hello Hunsy" he said
"I hear you have a problem, your beans they look well fed!
I'll start working right away, it could take me several hours
The plants look very healthy, you've got loads of flowers".

Hunsy watered them every day, her beans began to grow
She's hoping to be on the tele: - on some agriculture show!
"One day I will become famous, my beans sold everywhere
Bertie the bee will help me out, when he's got time to spare".

Her beans they tasted delicious, she eats them every day
They keep you fit and healthy, they help you work and play
Fast food it isn't good for you, it makes you put on weight!
Runner beans are fresh and green - perfect on your plate.

Bluey the Blowfly

Hunsy was getting angry, "Get out of here" she said
"Or I shall use my fly spray but I don't want you dead"
"Don't be so cruel" said Bluey, "I clear up lots of mess!
I lay my eggs on rotting food, my maggots eat the rest".

"You've got dirty feet" she said, "You tread everywhere
Then you settle on my food, when I've got none to spare!
I have to throw the food away, if you have laid some eggs
I think you'd better stay outside, and feed on other dregs".

"Okay I'll go" said Bluey, "I thought you were my friend
I know when I'm not wanted, I would never wish to offend!
I love the summer evenings, when the doors are open wide
I always find somewhere to stay, and then I quickly hide".

"When people have a BBQ - we spread the word around!
My pals they all get ready, to bombard them on the ground
When the food is on their plates, we settle on all we can!
We don't get invited to parties - they've all put up a ban".

Rogue Rabbits

Hunsy was getting really upset, "Who's digging up my lawn?
It must be the rabbits living next door, too many babies are born
They've dug large holes in the meadow, all around the trees!
Someone could have an accident, and fall down on their knees".

Hunsy filled the holes with earth, it was really a waste of time
Every night the culprits came back, to continue with their crime!
"I need to stop them" she said to Thumps, "Everything will suffer
They're very naughty baby rabbits, we need a law that's tougher".

"We must consult Ollie the owl, he deals with neighbour disputes
Every time he wins his case, he stands up in the court and Hoots"
"I'll be a witness", said Pip the squirrel, "I always get the blame
I saw the rabbits digging up the grass, I need to clear my name".

Hunsy didn't know what to do, she put up a large notice board!
'Trespassers will be prosecuted', these vandals she couldn't afford
If the rabbits ignored the warning sign, she'd issue a stiff penalty
They would never be welcome again - to visit 'Bide a Wee'.

Lennie the Leaf Collector

Hunsy opened the garage door, "Come on Lennie" she said
"We've got lot's of work to do, you can't laze there in your bed
The leaves are falling very fast, they're covering all the ground
Whirly the wind is helping them, he blows them all around".

Lennie said "Don't worry, I'm beginning to feel very hungry
I haven't eaten for so long now, I don't usually work on Sunday"
"I know" said Hunsy "But Renee the rain is turning up tomorrow
You really need to do this job, as loads more leaves will follow".

Hunsy plugged his lead in, his motor, it sounded quite loud!
"I'm all ready to get going" he said, he stood there very proud
His wide funnel sucks up the leaves, they don't stand a chance
Whirly loves to blow them around, he causes a merry dance.

Hunsy always guides Lennie, he has two little wheels in front
The leaves get mulched into his bag, made ready for the dump
The two of them work well together, Lennie just clears the lot!
Binny the dustbin likes helping out - he gets filled to the top.

Gordon the Green Waste Bin

Gordon stood there upright, he's a new kid on the block
"I collect all the green waste, sometimes I'm choc a block!
I was trained in the Army, by the sergeant major's drill
We were all taught discipline, we learned a lot of skill".

"Now I'm back in Civie Street, I live with Colin next door
Soon there will be an army of bins, we're really out to score!
He fills me up with his green waste, branches from the trees
I work hard all summertime, I'm always ready to please".

Hunsy is rather old fashioned she doesn't want a large bin
She's very loyal to Binny the dustbin, she's very fond of him
He enjoys going to the tip, on the front seat of Hunsy's car!
He has a chat with the other bins, some have travelled far.

"Councils waste money" said Gordon "With so many bins!
But we don't want to be unemployed, that way nobody wins
One day we'll all be recycled, I can't see much future for us
Piles of plastic everywhere, for now we won't make a fuss".

Hunsy goes to the Tip

Hunsy cut the grass today, she could do with a skip!
She uses the recycling boxes, then they all go to the tip
Hunsy heard them arguing, the boxes were most upset
"We're going to get really dirty, the grass is very wet".

Binny the dustbin said, "Hunsy will hose you down!
Its fun going out for a ride, you shouldn't really frown
I'm happy we are working, others are still unemployed"
The boxes sat on the back seat, looking most annoyed.

"Its all right for you, you're older, we are almost new
Hunsy shouldn't abuse us like this, we have a job to do!
We collect all the plastic stuff, along with the metal tins
We're employed by the Council - very important bins!".

Binny felt he'd heard enough, "Hunsy needs our help
Just stop all this silly arguing, and fasten your safety belt
You'll enjoy the journey, maybe you'll meet new friends
It's always busy at the tip, the road has winding bends".

Halloween

Hunsy was getting excited, "It's Halloween night tonight
We're going to have a party, we'll give everyone a fright!
The witch living in the magic tree, she'll be flying around
Ollie the owl, will hoot all night, making an eerie sound".

"Hilda and Spud the spiders, will spin webs everywhere
It's going to be very frightening, as everyone we'll scare!
Batty the Bat will whiz around, flying near people's heads
She looks just like a vampire - fear she always spreads!".

"Scary the Scarecrow will join us, he loves having fun
He'll put a white sheet, over his head, scaring everyone!
We will need a large pumpkin, all brightly lit up inside
Farmer John he grows them, it fills him up with pride".

"The gnomes light up their cabins, a pretty sight to see!
The witch then casts her magic spells, here at 'Bide aWee'
She dances around her bonfire, the flames leap up so high!
Everyone's invited - there'll be a bright moon in the sky".

Hoppy cleans the Fences

Hunsy was cleaning the fences, Hoppy the Hose didn't mind
"Beaky the Pigeon is messy" he said, "I don't mean to be unkind"
Hoppy was really enjoying himself, "I'll wash around everywhere!
Beaky's been eating too much bread, he never wants to share".

"Now Now Hoppy" said Hunsy, "He's a member of our family
It's a nuisance he's making such a mess, he should use a lavatory"
Hoppy laughed at Hunsy, "You should stop him making this mess!
It doesn't really bother me, as it's you who's getting the stress".

Hoppy was singing as he worked, "I'm cleaning up everywhere"
He quickly hosed the fences down, there wasn't a moment to spare
"I'll water the flowers as I go along, Rene the Rain's still in Spain"
Hunsy was hoping she'd turn up, "Beaky's sure to do it again".

Hunsy was pleased with Hoppy, the fences looked really clean
He had washed all the mess away, the cleanest they'd ever been!
Then Beaky landed on the fence, Hunsy smiled and said, "Hello"
Beaky he looked very guilty - "I'm sorry but now I must go".

Puddles the Goldfish

Puddles swam alongside Donnie, "I'll soon be as big as you"
"Don't be silly" said Donnie the fish, "You haven't got a clue
No matter how much food you eat, you'll only put on weight!
You'll never grow as big as me, you're making a big mistake".

Puddles thought he must be right, "I will never look like him
I'll lose some weight gradually, as I've got to be able to swim!"
Hunsy was cleaning around the pond, "Hello Puddles" she said
You're looking really beautiful, you're healthy and well fed".

"Do you think I'm fat?" said Puddles, "I have been eating a lot
I wanted to be like Donnie the fish but I think I've lost the plot"
Fish come in all shapes and sizes, Koi Carp can grow very large
Gold fish are more ornamental, Donnie, he's built like a barge.

Hunsy bought two baby koi, they're growing up very fast!
Goldie and Patch swim together, Puddles feels he's an outcast
"I'm the only gold fish in the pond but they never bother me"
"You are special to them" said Hunsy, "Part of their family".

Hunsy in a Panic!

As winter time approaches, Hunsy gets very distressed!
She knows that Hector the heron's about, he really is a pest
"The pond it should be covered", She explained to Thumps
"It really is a problem" but she knew he'd come up trumps.

He made some frames for the pond, they were a perfect fit
"The wood is very strong" he said, "so they will never split"
He laid them on the top of the pond, it all looked very neat!
"I'll staple netting to the frames, to make the job complete".

Hunsy felt the fish were safe, with no need for her to worry
She went to bed and slept soundly but she awoke in a hurry
When she looked from her window, she had an awful shock!
Hector the heron, was on the new frames, ready to eat the lot.

Hunsy dashed down the garden, Hector flew quickly away
The fish were very frightened but Donnie said, "We're okay!"
Thumps stapled the nett onto the frames, Hector didn't score
He was cross he sulked all day, the fish now safe once more.

Thumps flies off to Spain

"Have you heard the latest news", Hector the heron jeered!
"Thumps has left Hunsy forever, he's gone and disappeared"
"It's very sad" said Pip the squirrel, "She'll be on her own!
He's always been there for her, how the time has flown".

"He won't worry" said Hector, "He's moving miles away
I reckon he's seeing someone else but doesn't want to say!
I was fishing out at sea, when I saw a plane bound for Spain
I saw Thumps through a window, we won't see him again".

Hunsy could hear them gossiping "I'm okay here" she said
"I've still got you all my family, it's the winter time I dread
It gets sweltering hot in sunny Spain, it wouldn't do for me!
The climate here is much nicer, especially when it's sunny".

Thumps was there for Hunsy, he helped her pave the way
She will always think of him, fond memories there to stay!
Now everyone can laugh with them, they only need to look
Hunsy and Thumps still together - embedded in a book.

We hope you have enjoyed this book
The stories, the pictures, the fun!
Please tell all your friends about us
We'll always make them welcome.

Rhyming Stories by Hazel M Foster

Illustrated by Dawn S Taylor

Animal and Garden Adventures

Hunsy, Thumps and Friends!

Volume 2

Author

Hazel M Foster

I dedicate this book to my friend Gerda

91032957R00046

Made in the USA
Columbia, SC
12 March 2018